BEATLES BIG NOTE

USA ISBN 0-8256-2299-9   USA Code 020273-9
UK ISBN 0-86001-038-4   UK Code NO-1740-2

Exclusive distributors:
Music Sales Limited, 8/9 Frith Street, London W1V 5TZ, England.
Music Sales Corp, 24 East 22nd Street, New York, NY 10010, U.S.A.
Music Sales Pty Limited, 27 Clarendon Street, Artarmon, Sydney, NSW 2064, Australia.

AMSCO PUBLICATIONS
London/New York/Sydney

Across The Universe

Starting note for singing:

Slowly

Words and Music by
JOHN LENNON and
PAUL McCARTNEY

Words are fly - ing out like end - less rain in to a pa - per cup, They slith - er while they pass, they slip a - way a - cross the u - ni - verse.

Pools of sor - row, waves of joy are drift - ing through my o - pen mind, pos - sess - ing and ca - ress - ing me. Jai____ Gu - ru____

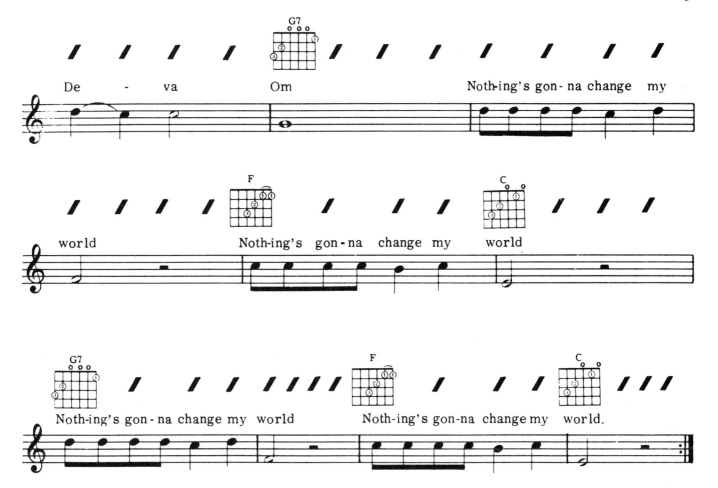

De - va   Om   Noth-ing's gon-na change my

world   Noth-ing's gon-na change my world

Noth-ing's gon-na change my world   Noth-ing's gon-na change my world.

Images of broken light
Which dance before me like a million eyes,
That call me on and on
Across the universe

Thoughts meander like a restless wind inside a letter box
They tumble blindly as they make their way
Across the universe

Sounds of laughter shades of earth
Are ringing through my open views
Inciting and inviting me.

Limitless undying love
Which shines around me like a million suns
It calls me on and on
Across the universe.

Jai __ Gu - ru __ De - va.

Keep repeating till fade

All My Loving

Words and Music by
JOHN LENNON and
PAUL McCARTNEY

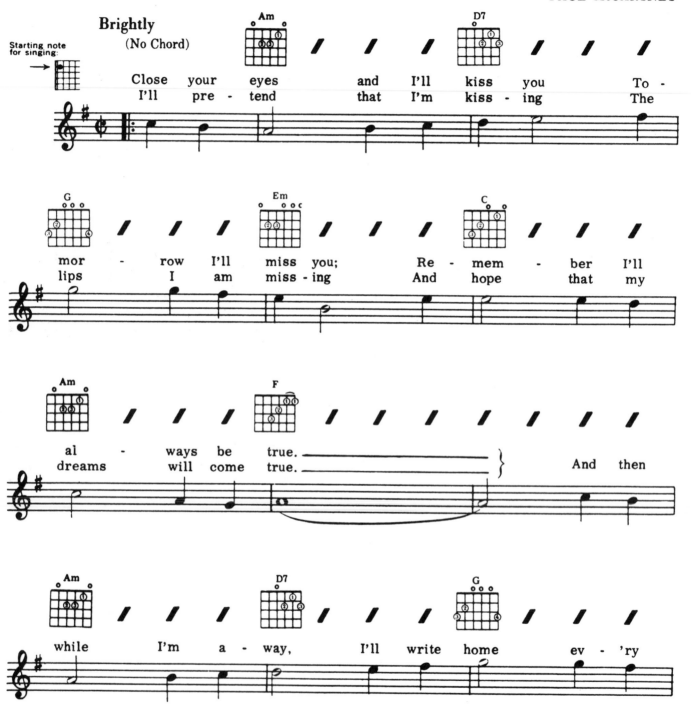

5

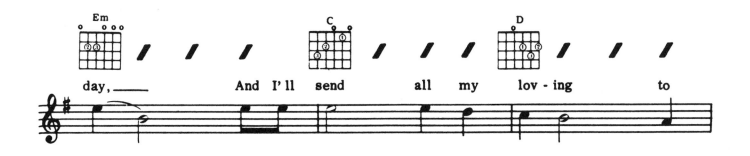

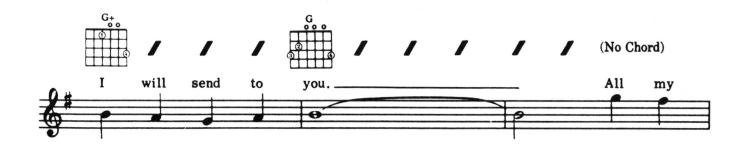

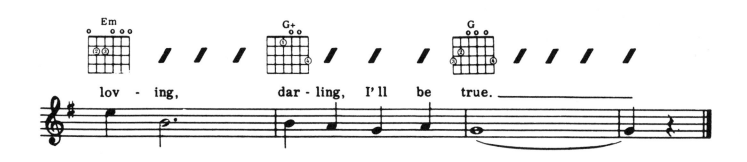

All Together Now

Words and Music by
JOHN LENNON and
PAUL McCARTNEY

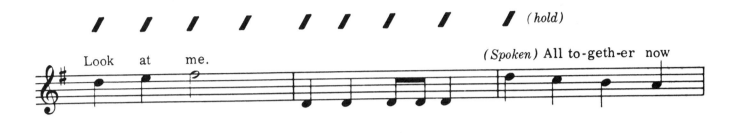

Look at me.
(Spoken) All to-geth-er now

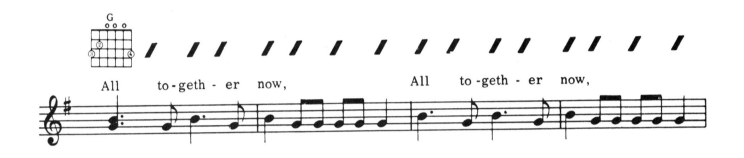

All to-geth-er now,
All to-geth-er now,

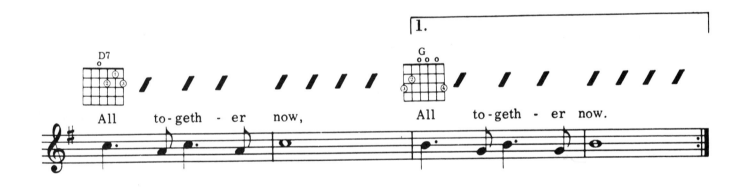

All to-geth-er now,
All to-geth-er now.

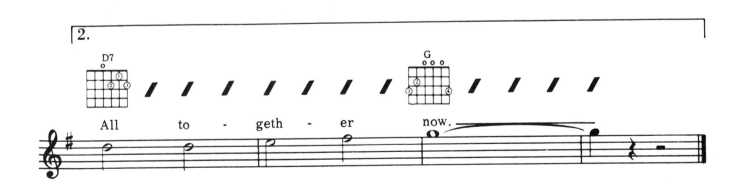

All to-geth-er now.

All You Need Is Love

Starting note for singing:

Words and Music by
JOHN LENNON and
PAUL McCARTNEY

And I Love Her

By
JOHN LENNON and
PAUL McCARTNEY

Can't Buy Me Love

Words and Music by
JOHN LENNON and
PAUL McCARTNEY

I'll buy you a dia-mond ring, my friend if it makes you feel al-
I'll give you all I've got to give if you say you love me

right, I'll get you an-y-thing my friend, if it
too, I may not have a lot to give, but what I've

makes you feel al-right, } For I don't care too much for mon-ey, for
got I'll give to you,

1. mon-ey can't buy me love. **2.** love. Can't buy me love,

Ev-'ry-bod-y tells me so, can't buy me love.

Carry That Weight

Starting note
for singing:

Words and Music by
JOHN LENNON and
PAUL McCARTNEY

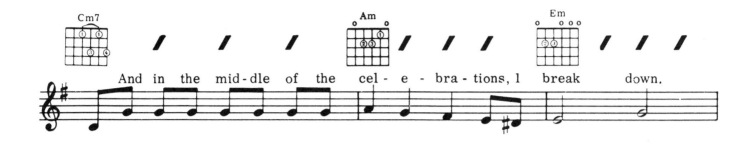

And in the mid-dle of the cel - e - bra - tions, I break down.

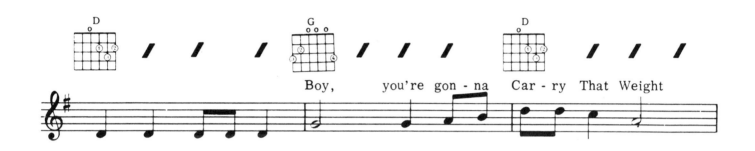

Boy, you're gon - na Car - ry That Weight

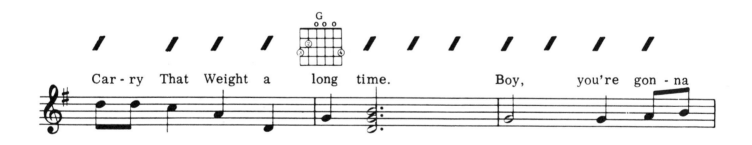

Car - ry That Weight a long time. Boy, you're gon - na

Car - ry That Weight Car - ry That Weight a long time.

Come Together

Words and Music by
JOHN LENNON and
PAUL McCARTNEY

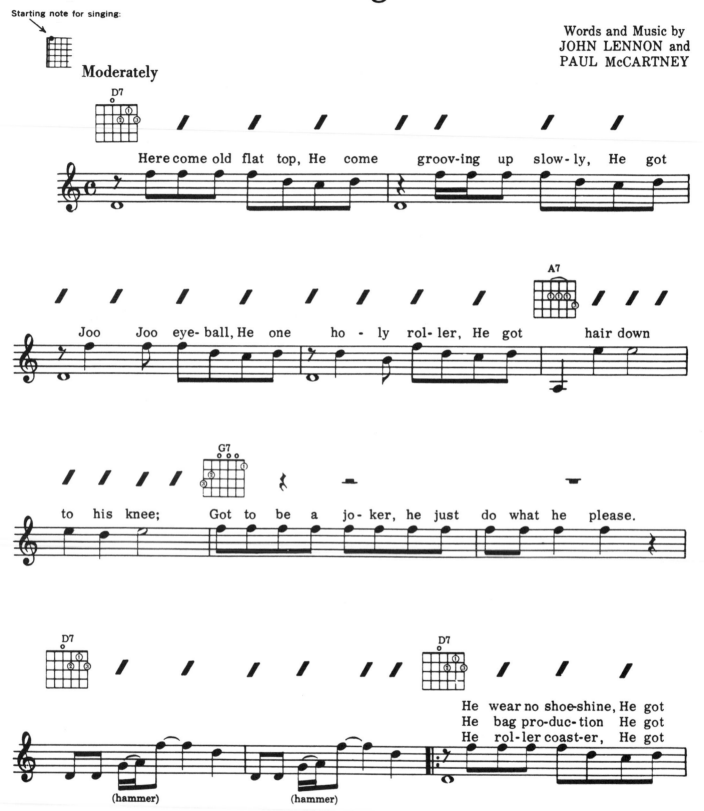

Here come old flat top, He come groov-ing up slow-ly, He got

Joo Joo eye-ball, He one ho-ly rol-ler, He got hair down

to his knee; Got to be a jo-ker, he just do what he please.

He wear no shoe-shine, He got
He bag pro-duc-tion He got
He rol-ler coast-er, He got

(hammer)   (hammer)

Come and Get It

Words and Music by
JOHN LENNON and
PAUL McCARTNEY

Day Tripper

Words and Music by
JOHN LENNON and
PAUL McCARTNEY

2. She's a big teaser, She took me half the way there.
She's a big teaser, She took me half the way there now.
She was a Day Tripper, One way ticket, Yeh!
It took me so long to find out, and I found out.

3. Tried to please her, She only played one night stands.
Tried to please her, She only played one night stands.
She was a Day Tripper, Sunday driver, Yeh!
It took me so long to find out, and I found out.

Eight Days A Week

Words and Music by
JOHN LENNON and
PAUL McCARTNEY

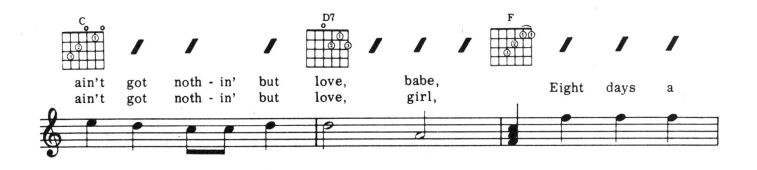

ain't got noth - in' but love, babe,
ain't got noth - in' but love, girl, Eight days a

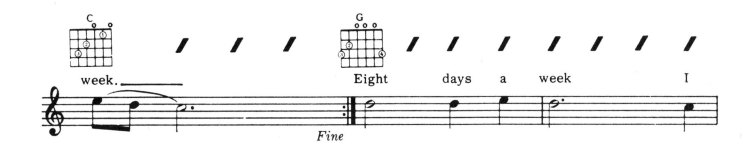

week. _____ Eight days a week I

Fine

love _____ you. _____ Eight days a

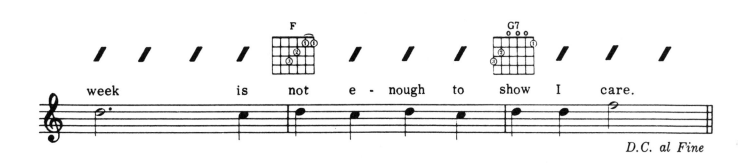

week is not e - nough to show I care.

D.C. al Fine

Eleanor Rigby

Words and Music by
JOHN LENNON and
PAUL McCARTNEY

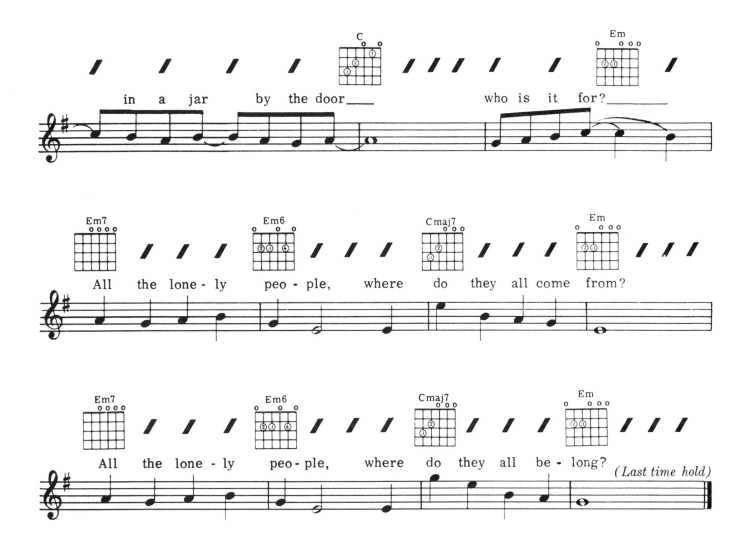

Father McKenzie, writing the words of a sermon that no one will hear, no one comes near.

Look at him working, darning his socks in the night when there's nobody there, what does he care?

All the lonely people, where do they all come from?

All the lonely people, where do they all belong?

Eleanor Rigby, died in the church and was buried along with her name, nobody came.

Father McKenzie, wiping the dirt from his hands as he walks from the grave, no one was saved.

All the lonely people, where do they all come from?

All the lonely people, where do they all belong?

Every Night

Moderately

Words and Music by
PAUL McCARTNEY

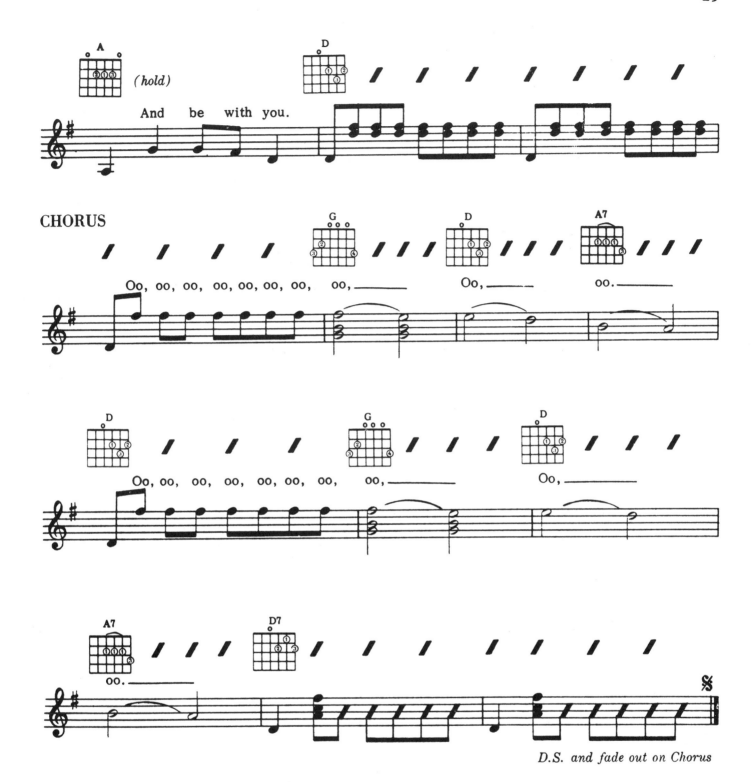

Ev'ry day I lean on a lamp-post,
I'm wasting my time.
Ev'ry night I lay on a pillow,
I'm resting my mind.
Ev'ry morning brings a new day
And ev'ry night that day is through oo - oo-oo-oo,
But tonight I just want to stay in and be with you,
And be with you.

Give Peace A Chance

Words and Music by
JOHN LENNON and
PAUL McCARTNEY

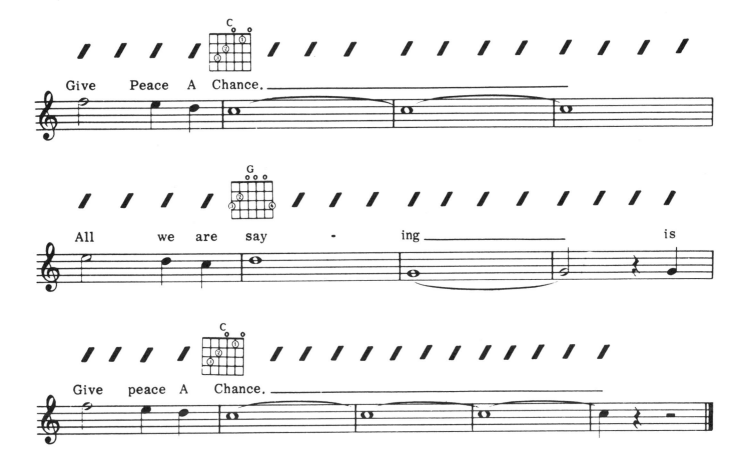

Give Peace A Chance.

All we are say - ing is

Give peace A Chance.

2. Ev'rybody's talking about
   Ministers, Sinisters, Banisters and Canisters,
   Bishops and Fishops, Rabbits and Popeyes,
   Bye-bye Bye-byes.

   All we are saying is Give Peace A Chance.
   All we are saying is Give Peace A Chance.

3. Let me tell you now,
   Ev'rybody's talking about
   Revolution, Evolution, Mastication, Flagellation,
   Regulations, Integregations, Meditation, United Nations,
   Congratulations.

   All we are saying is Give Peace A Chance.
   All we are saying is Give Peace A Chance.

4. Oh, let's stick to it,
   Ev'rybody's talking about
   John and Yoko, Timmy Leary, Rosemary, Tommy Smothers,
   Bobby Dylan, Tommy Cooper, Derek Taylor, Norman Mailer,
   Alan Ginsberg, Hare Krishna, Hare, Hare Krishna.

   All we are saying is Give Peace A Chance.
   All we are saying is Give Peace A Chance.
   All we are saying is Give Peace A Chance.
   All we are saying is Give Peace A Chance.

Goodbye

Words and Music by
JOHN LENNON and
PAUL McCARTNEY

Moderately Bright

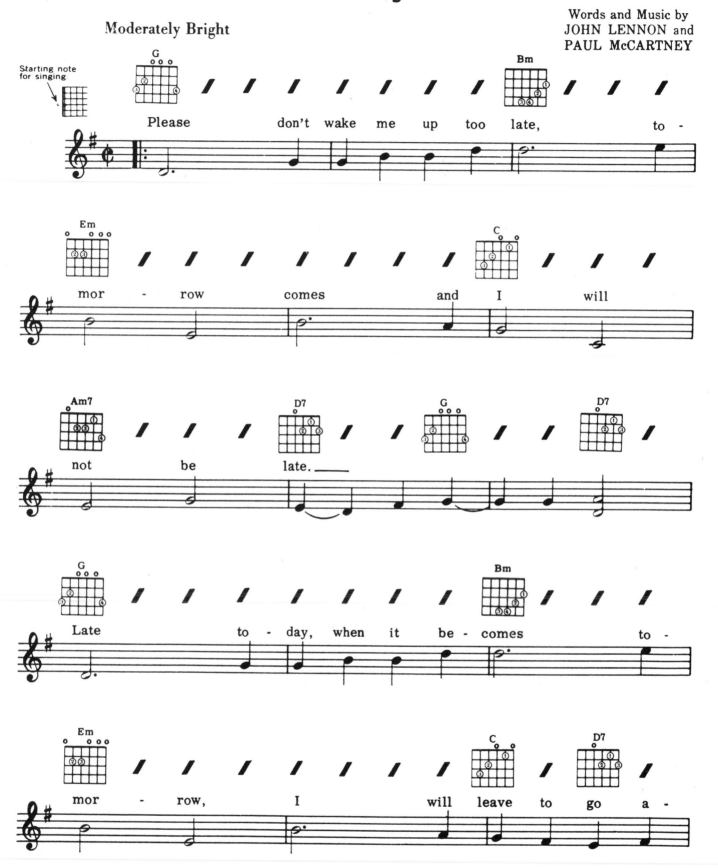

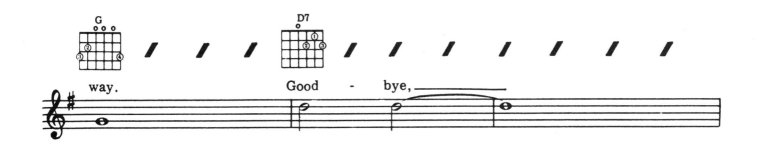

Songs that lingered on my lips
Excite me now and linger on my mind.
Leave your flowers at my door,
I'll leave them for the one who waits behind.
Goodbye, Goodbye, Goodbye,
Goodbye, my love, goodbye.

Far away, my lover sings a lonely song
And calls me to his side.
When a song of lonely love invites me on,
I must go to his side.
Goodbye, Goodbye, Goodbye,
Goodbye, my love goodbye.

Got To Get You Into My Life

Words and Music by
JOHN LENNON and
PAUL McCARTNEY

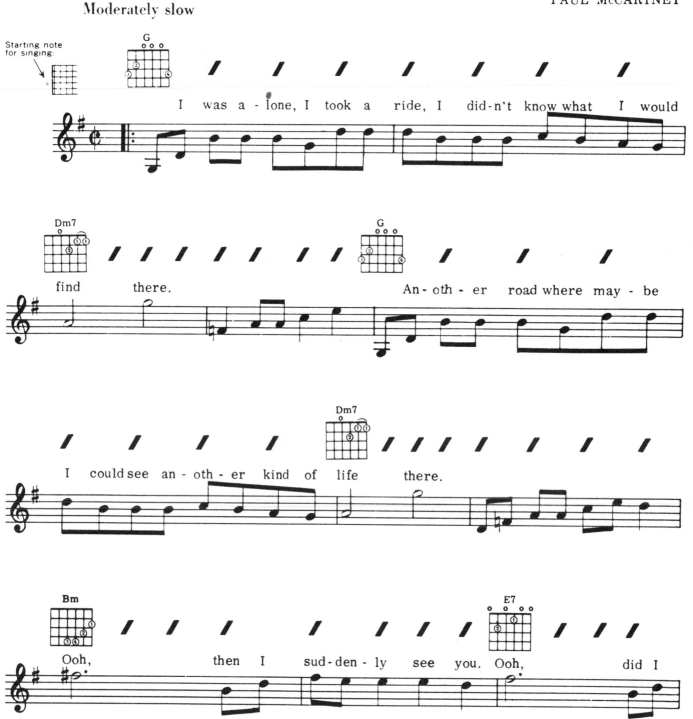

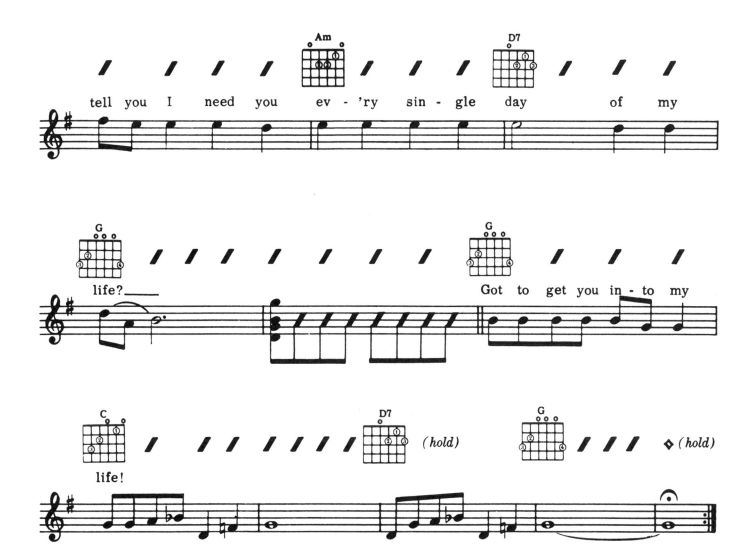

You didn't run, you didn't lie
You knew I wanted just to hold you.
And had you gone you knew in time
we'd meet again for I'd have told you.
Ooh, you were meant to be near me
Ooh, and I want you to hear me say
we'll be together ev'ry day.
Got to get you into my life!

What can I do, what can I be,
when I'm with you I want to stay there.
If I'm true I'll never leave and
if I do I know the way there.
Ooh, then I suddenly see you.
Ooh, did I tell you I need you
ev'ry single day of my life?
Got to get you into my life!

A Hard Day's Night

Words and Music by
JOHN LENNON and
PAUL McCARTNEY

Hello, Goodbye

Words and Music by
JOHN LENNON and
PAUL McCARTNEY

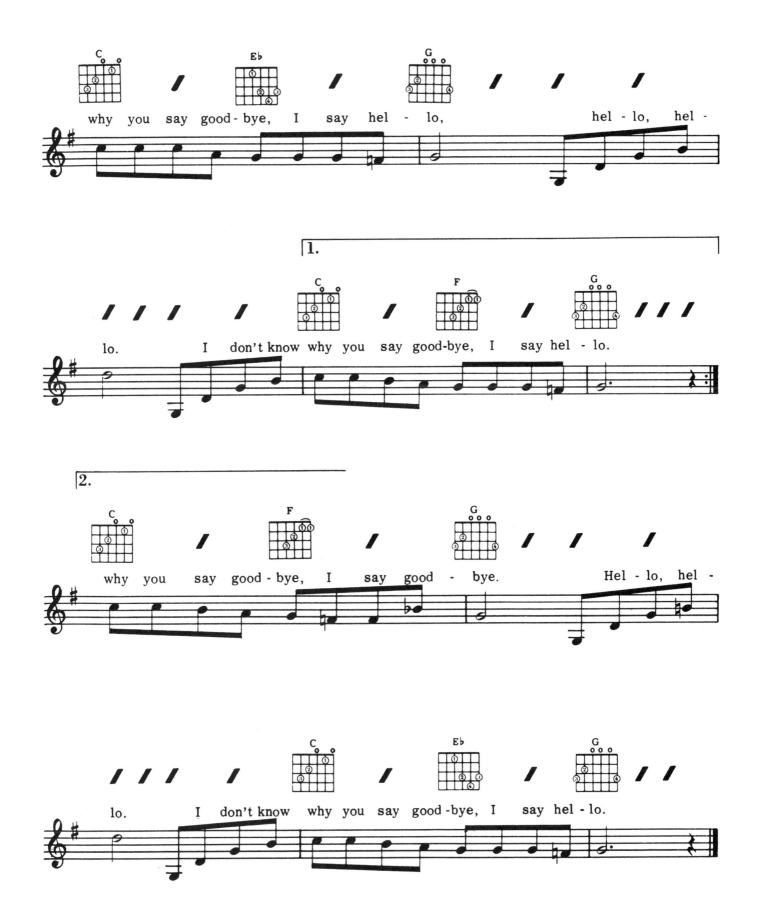

35

Help!

Words and Music by
JOHN LENNON and
PAUL McCARTNEY

Here, There And Everywhere

Words and Music by
JOHN LENNON and
PAUL McCARTNEY

Hey Jude

Words and Music by
JOHN LENNON and
PAUL McCARTNEY

Fade

I'm Happy Just To Dance With You

Words and Music by
JOHN LENNON and
PAUL McCARTNEY

In My Life

Words and Music by
JOHN LENNON and
PAUL McCARTNEY

Instant Karma

Words and Music by
JOHN LENNON

I've Got A Feeling

Words and Music by
JOHN LENNON and
PAUL McCARTNEY

Moderately slow

Starting note for singing:

I've got a feel - ing, a feel - ing deep in -

side, oh yeah, ___ oh

yeah. I've got a

feel - ing, a feel - ing I can't hide, oh no, ___

oh no, ___

(8th fret)

Coda

Ev-'ry-bod-y had a hard year, ev-'ry-bod-y had a
Ev-'ry-bod-y had a good year, ev-'ry-bod-y let their

good time, ev-'ry-bod-y had a wet dream, ev-'ry-bod-y saw the
hair down, ev-'ry-bod-y pulled-their socks up, ev-'ry-bod-y put their

sun shine, } , oh yeah, oh yeah, oh yeah.
foot down,

ad lib. "I've got a feeling" *etc.* (hold)

Play six times

Oh please believe me I'd hate to miss the train, oh yeah, oh yeah,
And if you leave me I won't be late again, oh no, oh no, oh no.
Yeah, Yeah, I've got a feeling, yeah!

I've got a feeling that keeps me on my toes, oh yeah, oh yeah.
I've got a feeling, I think that everybody knows, oh yeah, oh yeah, oh yeah.
Yeah, Yeah, I've got a feeling yeah!

Get Back

Words and Music by
JOHN LENNON and
PAUL McCARTNEY

Sweet Loretta Modern thought she was a woman,
But she was another man.
All the girls around her said she's got it coming,
But she gets it while she can.

Get back! Get back!
Get back to where you once belonged.
Get back' Get back'
Get back to where you once belonged.

Lady Madonna

Words and Music by
JOHN LENNON and
PAUL McCARTNEY

Moderately

Starting note for singing:

A   D   A   D

La - dy Ma - don - na, chil - dren at your feet

A   D   E   F   F   A   A

Won - der how you man - age to make ends meet?_____

Fine

A   D   A   D

Who finds the mon - ey when you pay the rent

A   D   E   F   F   A   A

Did you think that mon - ey was hea - ven sent?_____

D7   G7

Fri - day night ar - rives with - out a suit case,_____

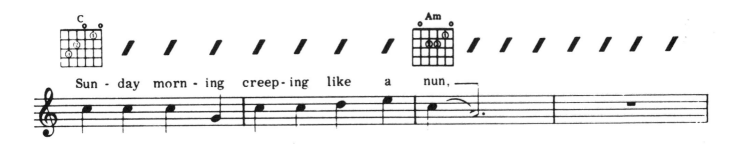

Sun - day morn - ing creep - ing like a nun, ——

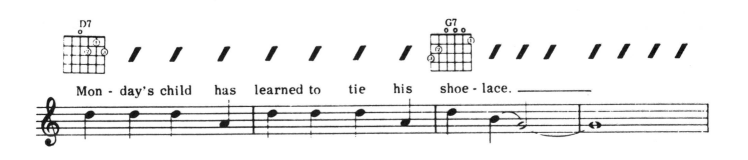

Mon - day's child has learned to tie his shoe - lace. ————

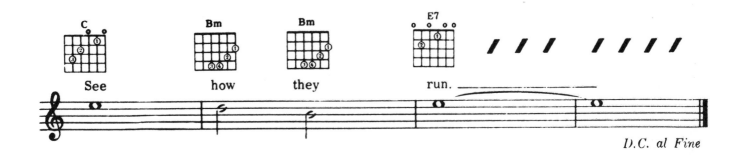

See how they run. ————

D.C. al Fine

Lady Madonna, baby at your breast,
Wonder how you manage to feed the rest.
Lady Madonna lying on the bed,
Listen to the music playing in your head.

Tuesday afternoon is never ending,
Wednesday morning papers didn't come,
Thursday night your stocking needed mending,
See how they run.

Let It Be

Words and Music by
JOHN LENNON and
PAUL McCARTNEY

2. And when the broken hearted people
Living in the world agree,
There will be an answer, let it be.
For tho' they may be parted
There is still a chance that they will see,
There will be an answer, let it be.
Let it be, let it be, let it be, let it be,
Yeah There will be an answer, let it be.
Let it be, let it be, let it, be, let it be,
Whisper words of wisdom, let it be.

3. And when the night is cloudy
There is still a light that shines on me,
Shine until tomorrow, let it be.
I wake up to the sound of music
Mother Mary comes to me,
Speaking words of wisdom, let it be.
Let it be, let it be, let it be, let it be,
Yeah There will be an answer, let it be.
Let it be, let it be, let it be, let it be,
Whisper words of wisdom, let it be.

The Long and Winding Road

Words and Music by
JOHN LENNON and
PAUL McCARTNEY

Michelle

Starting note for singing:

Moderately

Words and Music by
JOHN LENNON and
PAUL McCARTNEY

Michelle, ma belle, sont les mots qui vont tres bien ensemble, tres bien ensemble.
I need to, I need to, I need to, I need to make you see
Oh, what you mean to me. Until I do I'm hoping you will know what I mean.

I want you, I want you, I want you, I think you know by now
I'll get to you somehow. Until I do, I'm telling you so you'll understand,
My Michelle.

Maybe I'm Amazed

Words and Music by
PAUL McCARTNEY

Maybe I'm amazed at the way you're with me all the time,
And maybe I'm afraid of the way I need you.
Maybe I'm amazed at the way you help me sing my song,
    right me when I'm wrong,
And maybe I'm amazed at the way I really need you.

Norwegian Wood
(This Bird Has Flown)

Words and Music by
JOHN LENNON and
PAUL McCARTNEY

Fine

Nowhere Man

Words and Music by
JOHN LENNON and
PAUL McCARTNEY

Oh! Darling

Words and Music by
JOHN LENNON and
PAUL McCARTNEY

Oh! Darling, Please believe me,
I'll never let you down.
Believe me when I tell you,
I'll never do you no harm.

Paperback Writer

Words and Music by
JOHN LENNON and
PAUL McCARTNEY

un - der-stand. His son is work-ing for the Dail - y Mail; It's a

stead - y job, but he wants to be a pa - per - back

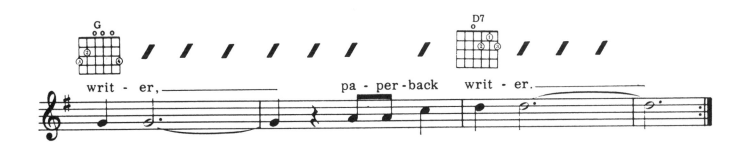

writ - er,_____ pa - per-back writ - er._____

It's a thousand pages, give or take a few,
I'll be writing more in a week or two.
I can make it longer if you like the style,
I can change it 'round and I want to be a paperback writer, paperback writer.
If you really like it you can have the rights,
It could make a million for you overnight.
If you must return it you can send it here;
But I need a break and I want to be a paperback writer, paperback writer

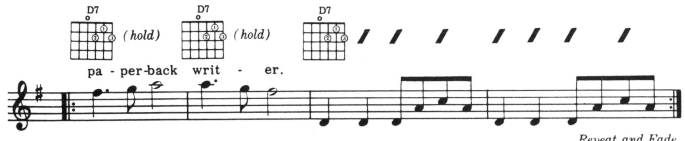

pa - per-back writ - er.

Repeat and Fade

Penny Lane

Words and Music by
JOHN LENNON and
PAUL McCARTNEY

Moderately Bright

Back in Penny Lane: there is a fireman with an hourglass.
And in his pocket is a portrait of the queen.
He likes to keep his fire engine clean, it's a clean machine.
Penny Lane is in my ears and in my eyes.
Full of fish and finger pies in summer meanwhile

Back behind the shelter in the middle of the round-a-bout
A pretty nurse is selling poppies from a tray.
And tho' she feels as if she's in a play she is anyway.
Back in Penny Lane: the barber shaves another customer.
We see the banker sitting waiting for a trend.
And the the fireman rushes in from the pouring rain, very strange.

Revolution

Words and Music by
JOHN LENNON and
PAUL McCARTNEY

Moderate Steady Beat

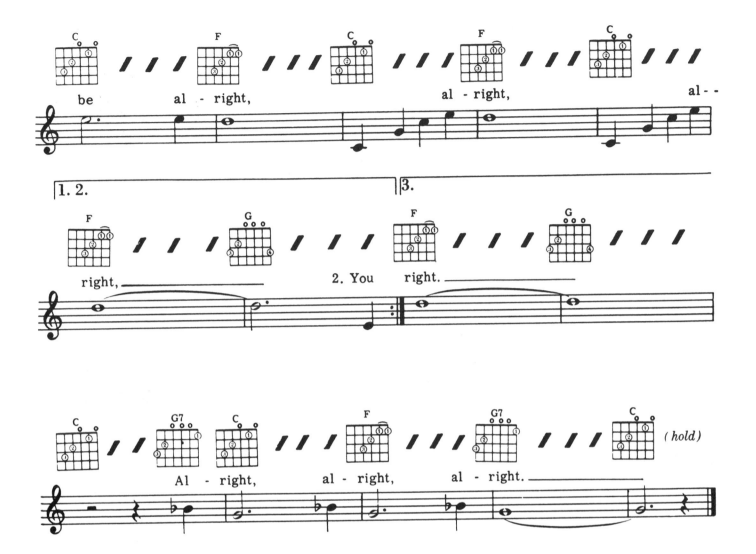

73

You say you got a real solution,
Well, you know, we'd all love to see the plan.
You ask me for a contribution.
Well, you know, We are doing what we can.
But when you want money for people with minds that hate,
All I can tell you is brother you have to wait
Don't you know it's gonna be alright, alright, alright,

You say you'll change the constitution,
Well, you know, We all want to change your head.
You tell me it's the institution.
Well, you know, You better free your mind instead.
But if you go carrying pictures of Chairman Mao,
You ain't going to make it with anyone anyhow,
Don't you know it's gonna be alright, alright, alright.

Ringo's Theme
(This Boy)

Words and Music by
JOHN LENNON and
PAUL McCARTNEY

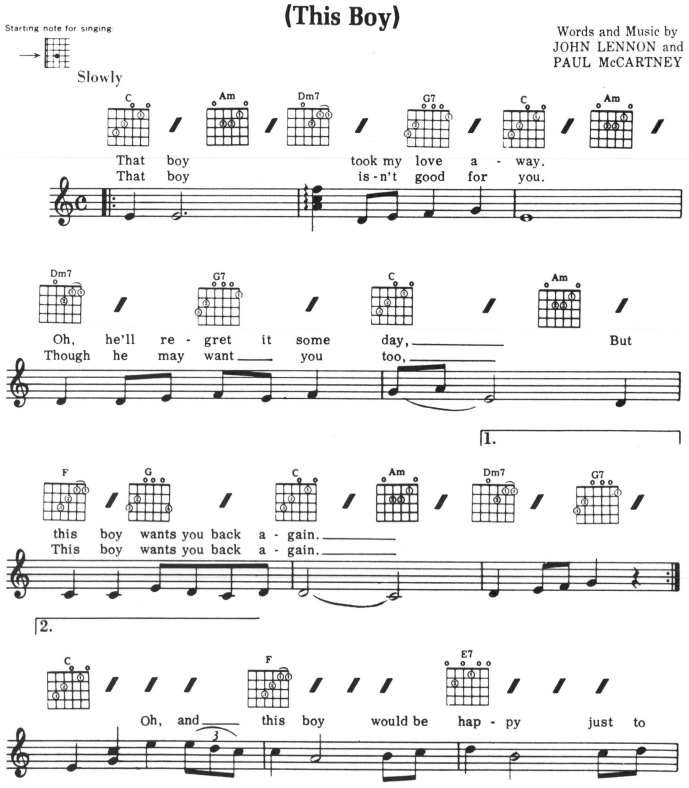

Repeat and fade out

Sgt. Pepper's Lonely Hearts Club Band

Words and Music by
JOHN LENNON and
PAUL McCARTNEY

Moderately Bright

CHORUS

She Came In
Through The Bathroom Window

Moderately Slow

Words and Music by
JOHN LENNON and
PAUL McCARTNEY

D.C. al Fine

The Lovely Linda

Words and Music by
PAUL McCARTNEY

Strawberry Fields Forever

Words and Music by
JOHN LENNON and
PAUL McCARTNEY

Let me take you down 'cause I'm goin' to
Strawberry Fields.
Nothing is real, and nothing to get hung about,
Strawberry fields forever.
No one I think is in my tree,
I mean it must be high or low.
That is you know you can't tune in but
it's all right.
That is, I think it's not too bad.

Let me take you down 'cause I'm goin' to
Strawberry Fields.
Nothing is real, and nothing to get hung about,
Strawberry fields forever.
Always know, sometimes think it's me.
But you know and I know it's a dream.
I think I know of thee, ah yes but it's all
wrong.
That is, I think I disagree.

Ticket To Ride

Words and Music by
JOHN LENNON and
PAUL McCARTNEY

1. I think I'm gon-na be sad, I think it's to-day,
2. 3. She said that liv-ing with me is bring-ing her down,

yeh! The girl that's driv-ing me mad is go-ing a - way.
yeh! For she would nev - er be free when I was a - round.

She's got a tick-et to ride,___ She's got a tick-et to ri - hi-hide, She's got a tick-et to ride, but she don't care.___

We Can Work It Out

Words and Music by
JOHN LENNON and
PAUL McCARTNEY

Moderately Slow

85

With A Little Help From My Friends

Moderately

Words and Music by
JOHN LENNON and
PAUL McCARTNEY

1. What would you do if I sang out of tune, would you
2. What do I do if when my love is a way, does it
3. Would you be - lieve in a love at first sight? Yes, I'm

stand up and walk out on me? Lend me your ears and I'll
wor - ry you to be a - lone? How do I feel by the
certain that it happens all the time. What do you see when you

sing you a song and I'll try not to sing out of key, Oh I get
end of the day are you sad be - cause you're on your own? No, I get
turn out the light? I can't tell you but I know it's mine. Oh, I get

by with a lit - tle help from my friends.
by with a lit - tle help from my friends.
by with a lit - tle help from my friends. Mm. I get

World Without Love

Words and Music by
JOHN LENNON and
PAUL McCARTNEY

She may come, I know not when, When she does I'll know, so ba - by un - til

then Lock me a - way And don't al - low the day here in -

side Where I hide with my lone - li - ness I don't

care what they say I won't stay in a world with-out love.

Yellow Submarine

Words and Music by
JOHN LENNON and
PAUL McCARTNEY

So we sailed up to the sun,
Till we found the sea of green,
And we lived beneath the waves,
In our Yellow Submarine. (Cho.)

And our friends are all aboard,
Many more of them live next door,
And the band begins to play. (Inst.)
(Chorus)

As we live a life of ease,
Everyone of us has all we need,
Sky of blue and sea of green,
In our Yellow Submarine. (Cho.)

Yesterday

Words and Music by
JOHN LENNON and
PAUL McCARTNEY

You've Got To Hide Your Love Away

Words and Music by
JOHN LENNON and
PAUL McCARTNEY

Moderato

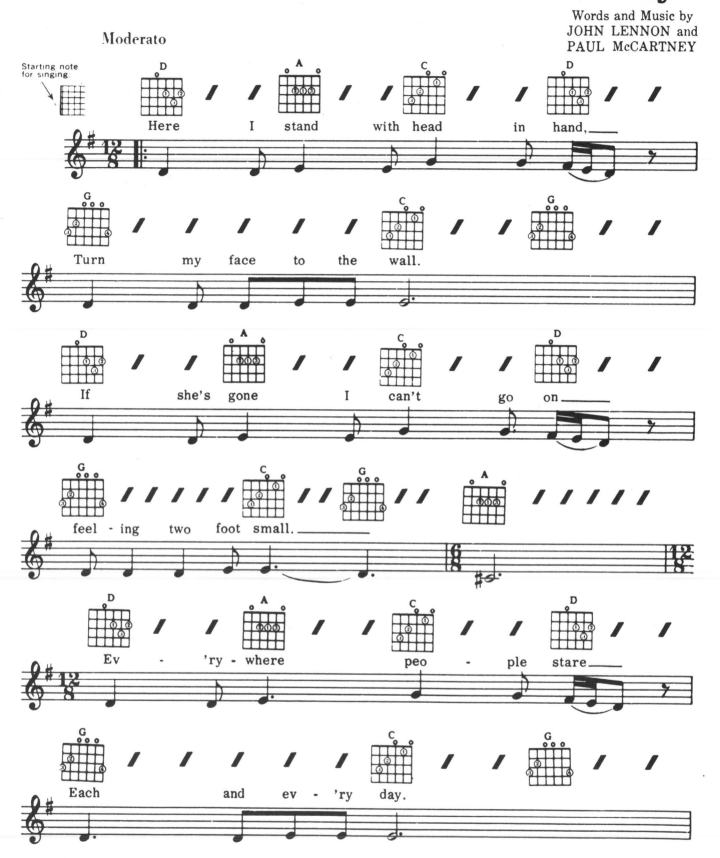

Here I stand with head in hand,

Turn my face to the wall.

If she's gone I can't go on

feel - ing two foot small.

Ev - 'ry - where peo - ple stare

Each and ev - 'ry day.

How can I even try?
I can never win.
Hearing them, seeing them
In the state I'm in.
How could she say to me,
"Love will find a way?"
Gather 'round, all you clowns,
Let me hear you say,
"Hey, you've got to hide your love away!
Hey, you've got to hide your love away!"

(Repeat and Fade)

That Would Be Something

Moderately

Words and Music by
PAUL McCARTNEY

Reproduced and printed by Halstan & Co. Ltd., Amersham, Bucks., England

10/86